WALLS DO TALK

POSTER BOOK

POSTERS TO ROCK YOUR LIFE!

FINE print
PUBLISHING

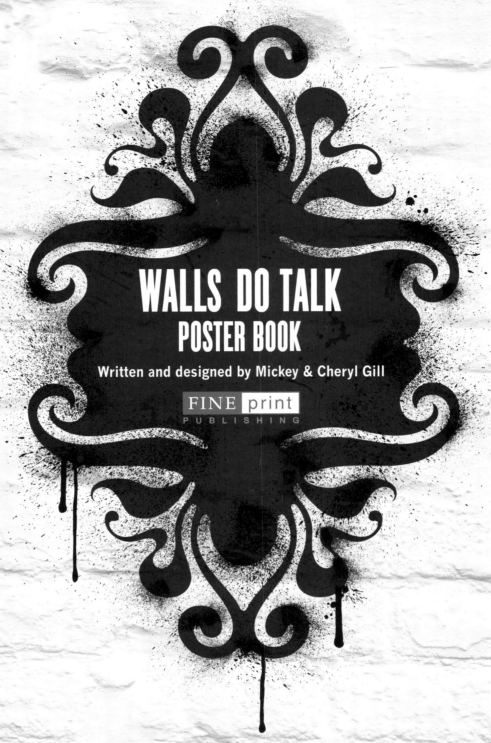

WALLS DO TALK
POSTER BOOK

Written and designed by Mickey & Cheryl Gill

FINE print
PUBLISHING

Fine Print Publishing Company
P.O. Box 916401
Longwood, Florida 32971-6401

Created in the U.S.A. & Printed in China
This book is printed on acid-free paper

ISBN 978-189295160-1

1 3 5 7 9 10 8 6 4 2

facebook.com/WallsDoTalk

MULTI-POSTER
MESSAGE
WITH OVER-THE-
TOP IMPACT

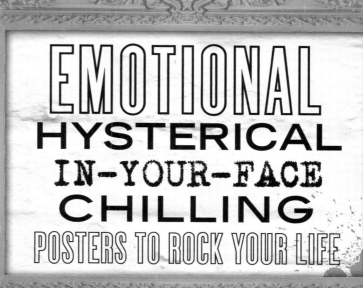

EMOTIONAL
HYSTERICAL
IN-YOUR-FACE
CHILLING
POSTERS TO ROCK YOUR LIFE

Create your own amazing scene with perforated posters ready to hang or frame.

SLIM
VERTICAL
MINI-CALENDARS
SIZED PERFECTLY
FOR LOCKERS

PLUS A DIY-FRAME
FOR YOUR FAVORITE!

Gently pull out each poster along perf

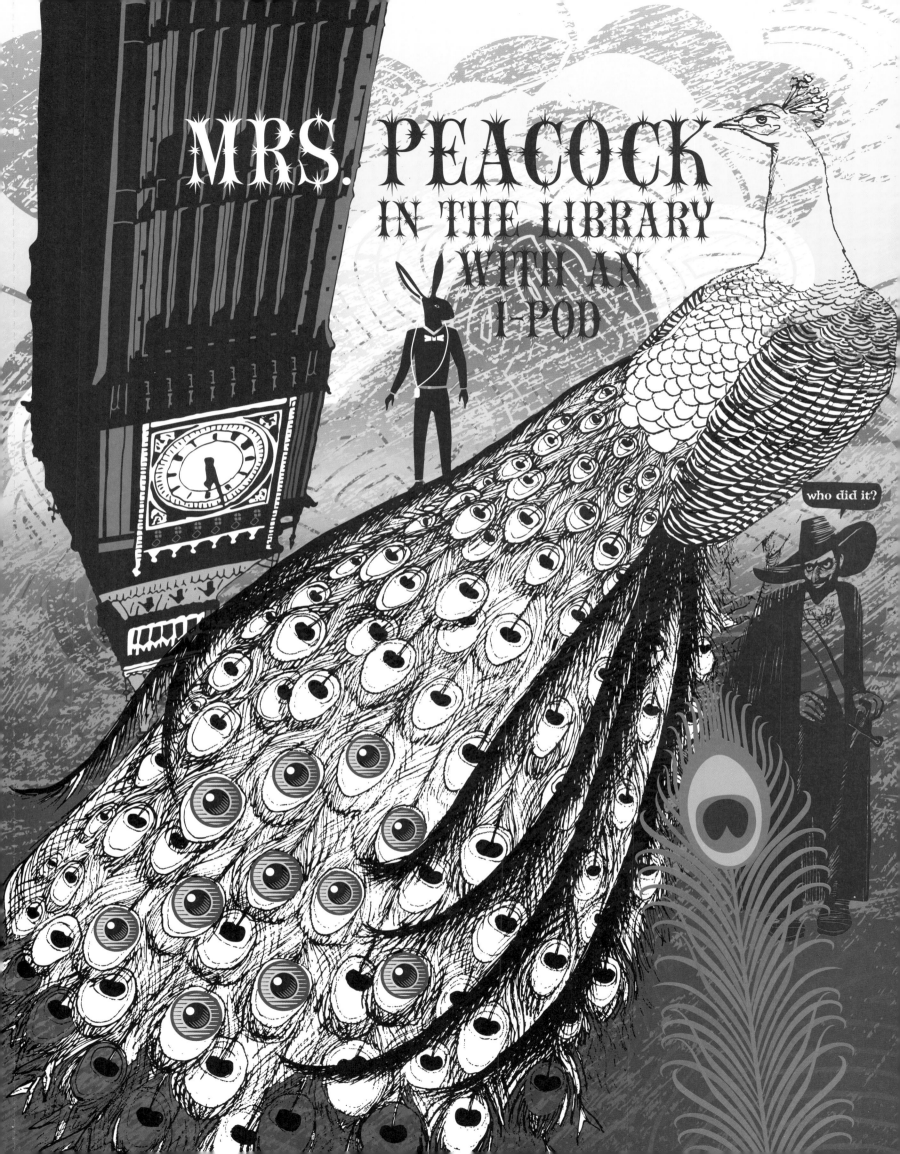

MISS SCARLET
IN THE LOUNGE
WITH A
DESIGNER
SHOE

less than three

ONCE UPON A TIME, I WANTED TO BE A FAIRY PRINCESS. THEN QUEEN FOR A DAY.

NOW I JUST WANT TO RULE THE WORLD FOREVER.

LOOK INTO MY EYES
YOU WILL DO WHAT
I TELL YOU.

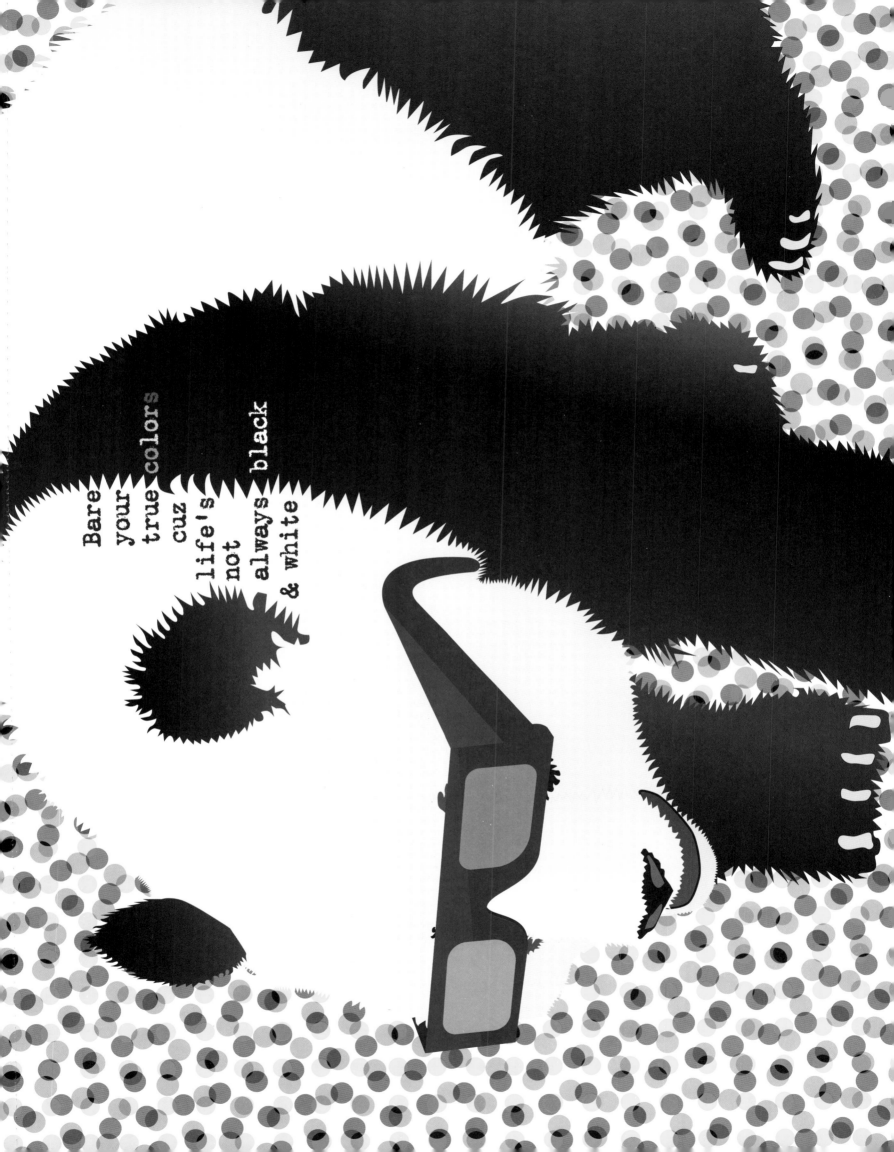

black and white

black and white

black and white

black and white

black and white

DON'T TOUCH MY EGG, PUNK

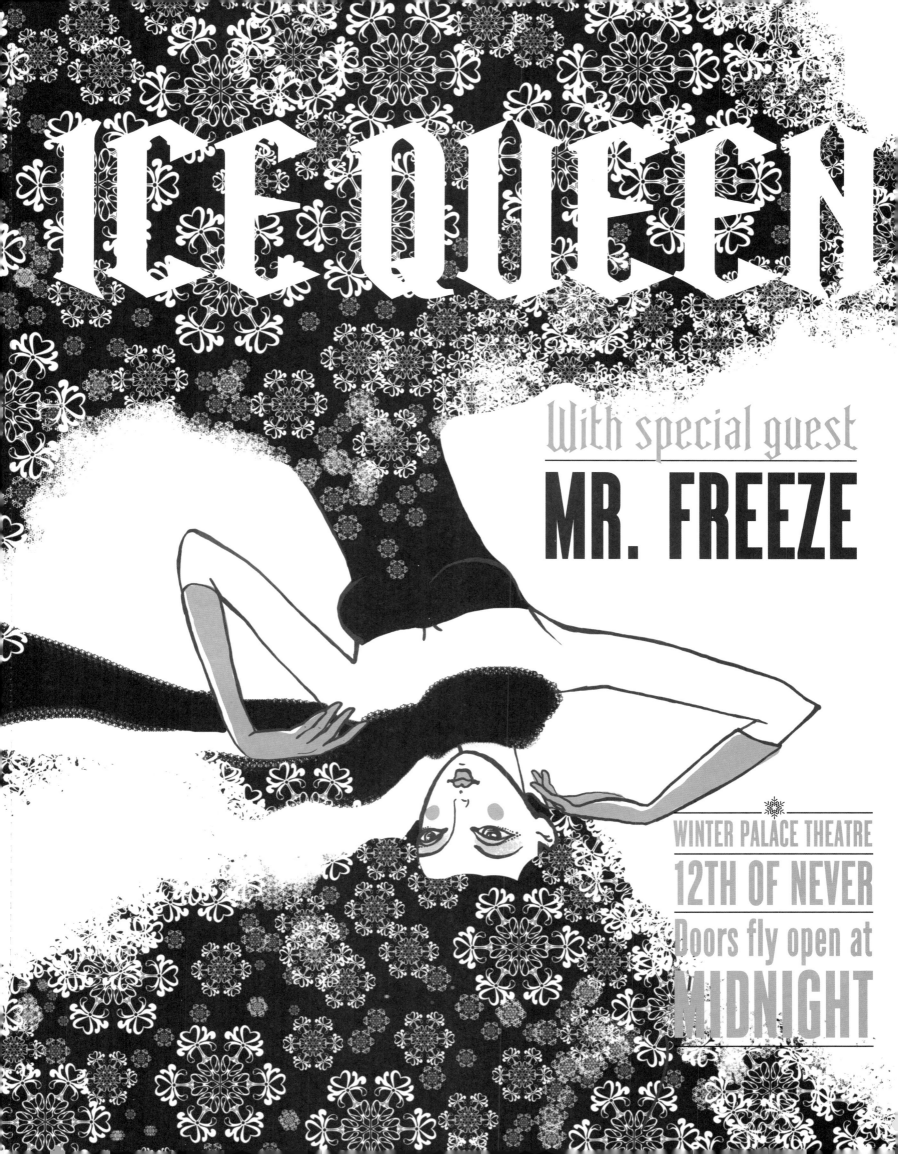

An Evening with
April Jewels
Flower Tower
Kissing Experiment

FEATURING

THE

BLOOMERS

MAY DAY | SPRINGVILLE SUPPER CLUB | ADMISSION: 5 CANS OF FOOD

STARTS AT EIGHT

BIG ISLAND LOVE

THE CRYPT
OCTOBER 31
10 pounds at the door

NEXT OF PUMPKIN appearing with
THE BATARANGS

Skeleton
key
to
my
heart

R

E 👁 A

D T H

E W R I

T I N G O

N T H E W A L L

━━━━━━━━━━━━━━━

B E L I E V E N O

T H I N G Y O U H E A

━━━━━━━━━━━━━━━

R A N D O N L Y H A L F

O F W H A T Y O U S E E

1

2

3

4

5

6

7

8

9

10

walls do talk

group hug?

PHRONEMOPHOBIA
THE FEAR OF THINKING

Linonophobia: A gloomy fear of strings!

LUTRAPHOBIA:
FEAR OF OTTERS

Nephophobia: Fear of clouds

SCIOPHOBIA: FEAR OF SHADOWS

PHOBOPHOBIA: AN EXCESSIVE FEAR OF ACQUIRING A PHOBIA

PHEARS & FOBIAS

XANTHOPHOBIA
FEAR OF THE COLOR YELLOW

ORTOGRAPHOBIA
Fear of spelling mistakes

Siderophobia is the fear of stars

CONSECOTALEOPHOBIA IS THE ABNORMAL FEAR OF CHOPSTICKS

PAPYROPHOBIA IS THE FEAR OF PAPER

PTERONOPHOBIA-FEAR OF BEING TICKLED BY FEATHERS

LEVOPHOBIA: FEAR OF THINGS TO THE LEFT SIDE OF THE BODY

ANTHROPHOBIA
FEAR OF FLOWERS

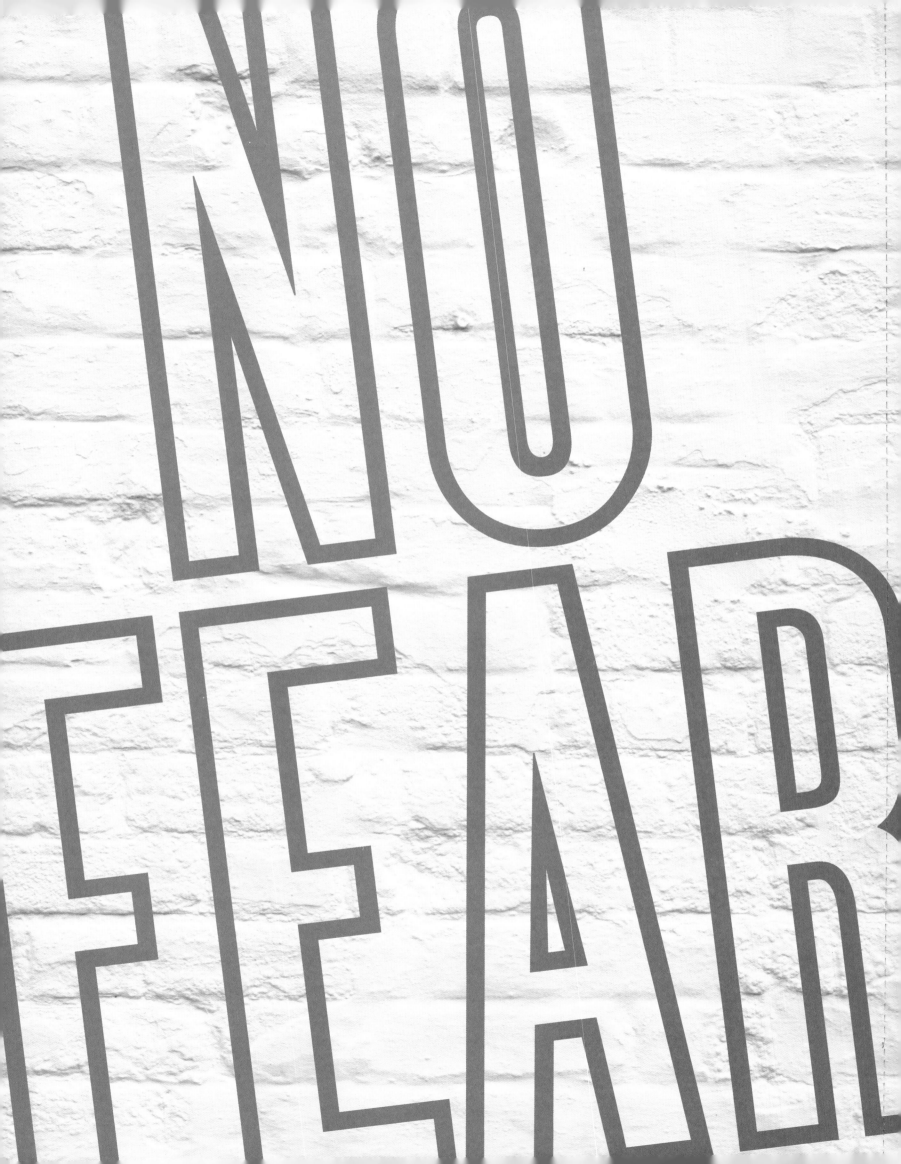

The Raven, Edgar Allan Poe

Nevermore

Open here I flung the shutter, when, with many a flirt and flutter,

in there stepped a stately raven

...other friends have
flown before ...

EAP

He'S moRe myself than I Am. WhatEver our sOuls aRe mAde of, his and Mine are tHe sAMe

Emily Bronte, Wuthering Heights

Heathcliff Catherine

Between me and the
moonlight flitted a great
bat, coming and going
in great, whirling circles.

— Bram Stoker, Dracula

BEAU
TIFUL
GIRL

beauty unmasked

LOVE ME!

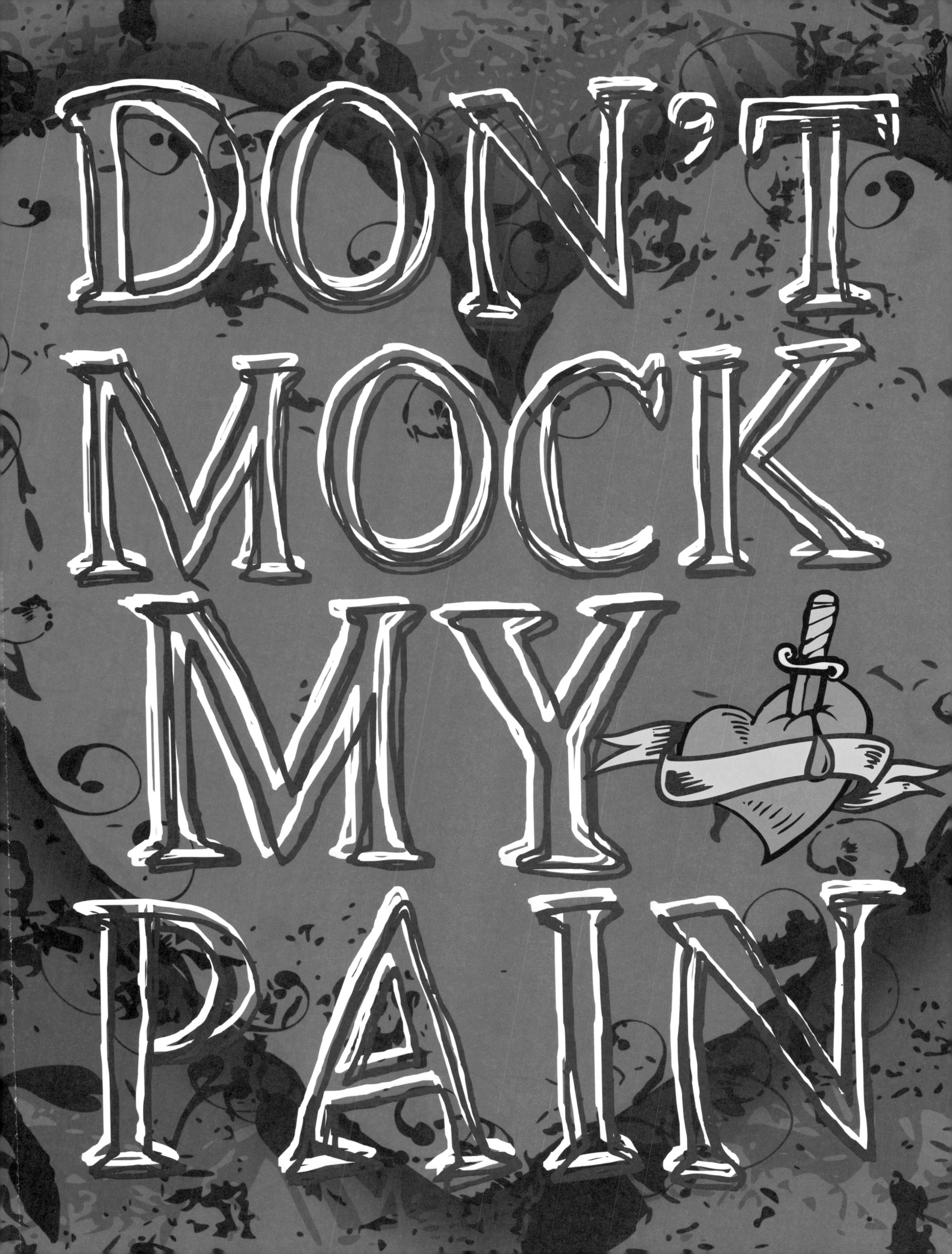
DON'T
MOCK
MY
PAIN

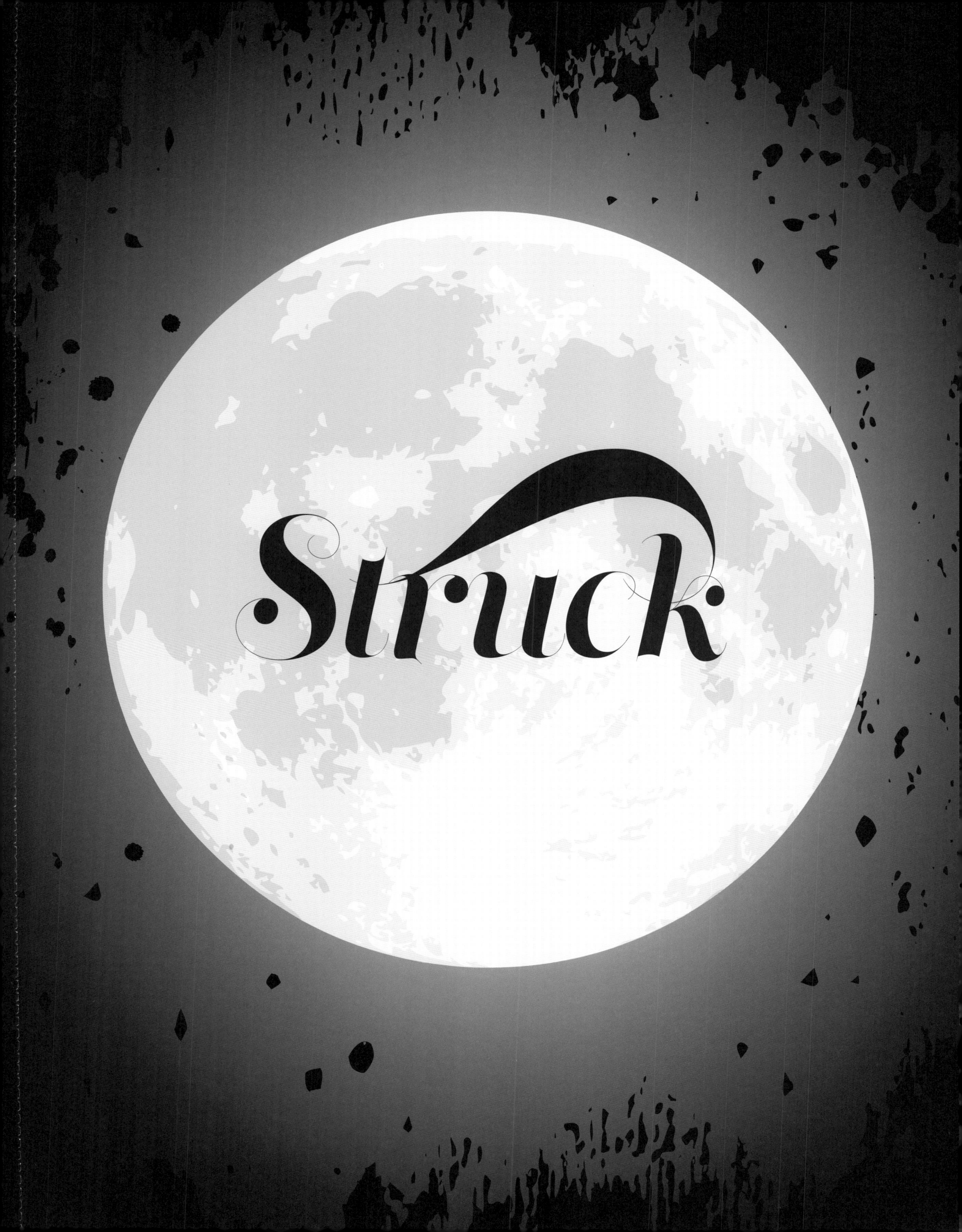
Struck

It's just a phase

what rocks your soul?

Just for TODAY let's shake it up a bit. Burst into song in public. Tell everyone you prefer to be called Mercury. When someone asks why you haven't done something, say you've been too busy designing a new app, then think of a new app. Karate chop some Styrofoam. Wear a nametag all day, wherever you go. Ask people if they've seen you because you've been looking everywhere for yourself. Pick out a star and name it. Place a drive-thru order of a burger with everything except the bun. Pop some bubble wrap. Paint stripes on your toenails. Write outrageous entries in a diary and then leave it unlocked.

make
2day
count

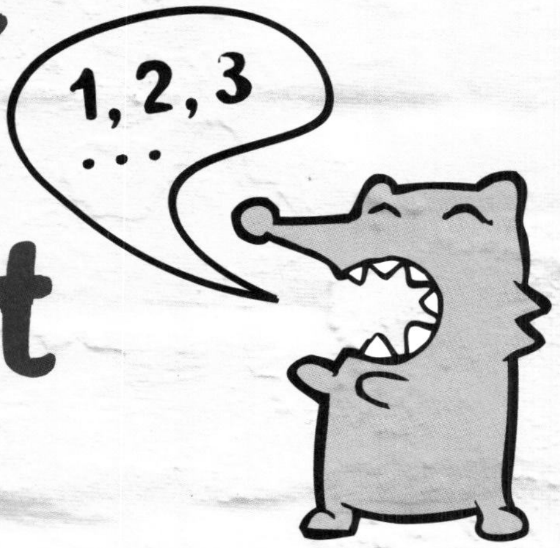

Arrange posters to send
out your message.

epic {'epik}

adjective
heroic or grand in scale or
character; legendary

ORIGIN late 16th cent. (as
an adjective): via Latin from
Greek epikos, from epos 'word,
song,' related to eipein 'say.'

EPIC song

don't blink

Cut poster in half.
Then cut out the speak
bubble that fits your
mood or fill in a
blank one.
Tape to poster.

Tear left side of butterfly poster out.
Gently loosen wing along perforated
line and bend slightly forward.
Repeat with right side of butterfly
poster. Tape together and hang.

Tear right side of butterfly poster out.
Gently loosen wing along perforated
line and bend slightly forward.
Repeat with left side of butterfly
poster. Tape together and hang.

1_____
2_____
3_____
4_____
5_____
6_____
7_____
8_____
9_____
10_____
11_____
12_____
13_____
14_____
15_____
16_____
17_____
18_____
19_____
20_____
21_____
22_____
23_____
24_____
25_____
26_____
27_____
28_____
29_____
30_____
31_____

01 JANUARY one

1_____
2_____
3_____
4_____
5_____
6_____
7_____
8_____
9_____
10_____
11_____
12_____
13_____
14_____
15_____
16_____
17_____
18_____
19_____
20_____
21_____
22_____
23_____
24_____
25_____
26_____
27_____
28_____
29_____
Leap year

02 FEBRUARY

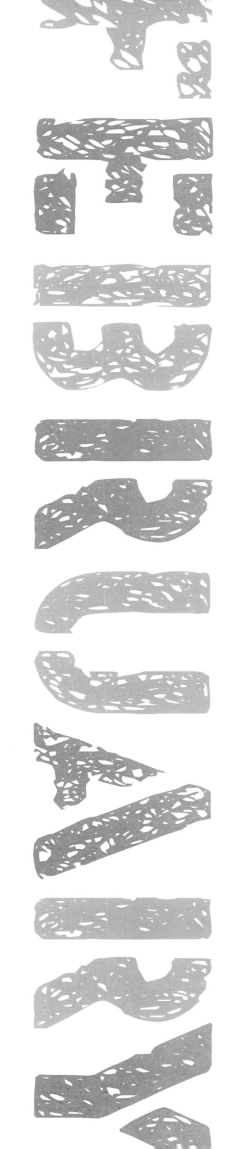

FEBRUARY

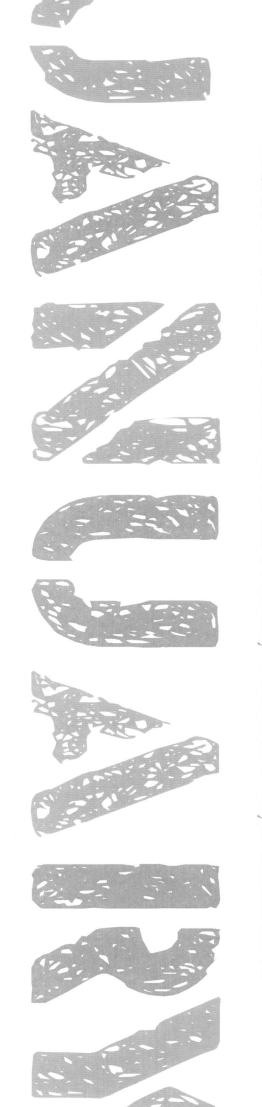

JANUARY

three

03

1_____
2_____
3_____
4_____
5_____
6_____
7_____
8_____
9_____
10_____
11_____
12_____
13_____
14_____
15_____
16_____
17_____
18_____
19_____
20_____
21_____
22_____
23_____
24_____
25_____
26_____
27_____
28_____
29_____
30_____
31_____

04

1_____
2_____
3_____
4_____
5_____
6_____
7_____
8_____
9_____
10_____
11_____
12_____
13_____
14_____
15_____
16_____
17_____
18_____
19_____
20_____
21_____
22_____
23_____
24_____
25_____
26_____
27_____
28_____
29_____
30_____

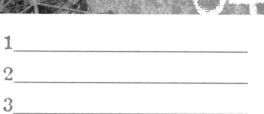

WRITE DOWN IMPORTANT DATES. HANG INSIDE LOCKER, ON BEDROOM DOOR, OR INSIDE ROOM.

WRITE DOWN IMPORTANT DATES. HANG INSIDE LOCKER, ON BEDROOM DOOR, OR INSIDE ROOM.

05 MAY five

1_____
2_____
3_____
4_____
5_____
6_____
7_____
8_____
9_____
10_____
11_____
12_____
13_____
14_____
15_____
16_____
17_____
18_____
19_____
20_____
21_____
22_____
23_____
24_____
25_____
26_____
27_____
28_____
29_____
30_____
31_____

06 JUNE six

1_____
2_____
3_____
4_____
5_____
6_____
7_____
8_____
9_____
10_____
11_____
12_____
13_____
14_____
15_____
16_____
17_____
18_____
19_____
20_____
21_____
22_____
23_____
24_____
25_____
26_____
27_____
28_____
29_____
30_____

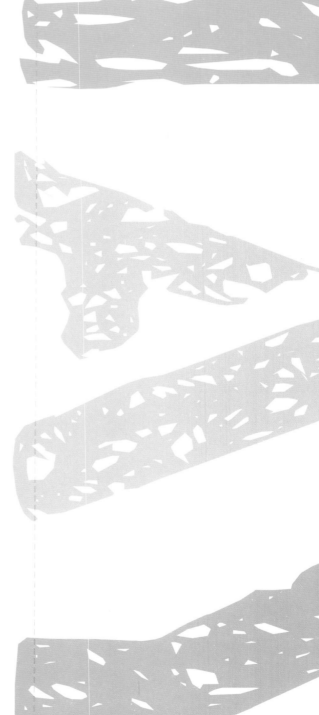

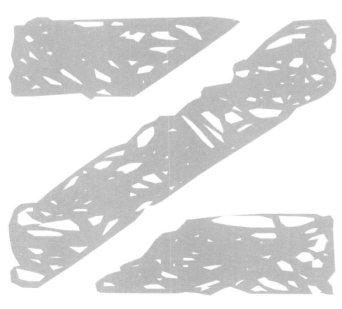

seven

1 _____
2 _____
3 _____
4 _____
5 _____
6 _____
7 _____
8 _____
9 _____
10 _____
11 _____
12 _____
13 _____
14 _____
15 _____
16 _____
17 _____
18 _____
19 _____
20 _____
21 _____
22 _____
23 _____
24 _____
25 _____
26 _____
27 _____
28 _____
29 _____
30 _____
31 _____

eight

1 _____
2 _____
3 _____
4 _____
5 _____
6 _____
7 _____
8 _____
9 _____
10 _____
11 _____
12 _____
13 _____
14 _____
15 _____
16 _____
17 _____
18 _____
19 _____
20 _____
21 _____
22 _____
23 _____
24 _____
25 _____
26 _____
27 _____
28 _____
29 _____
30 _____
31 _____

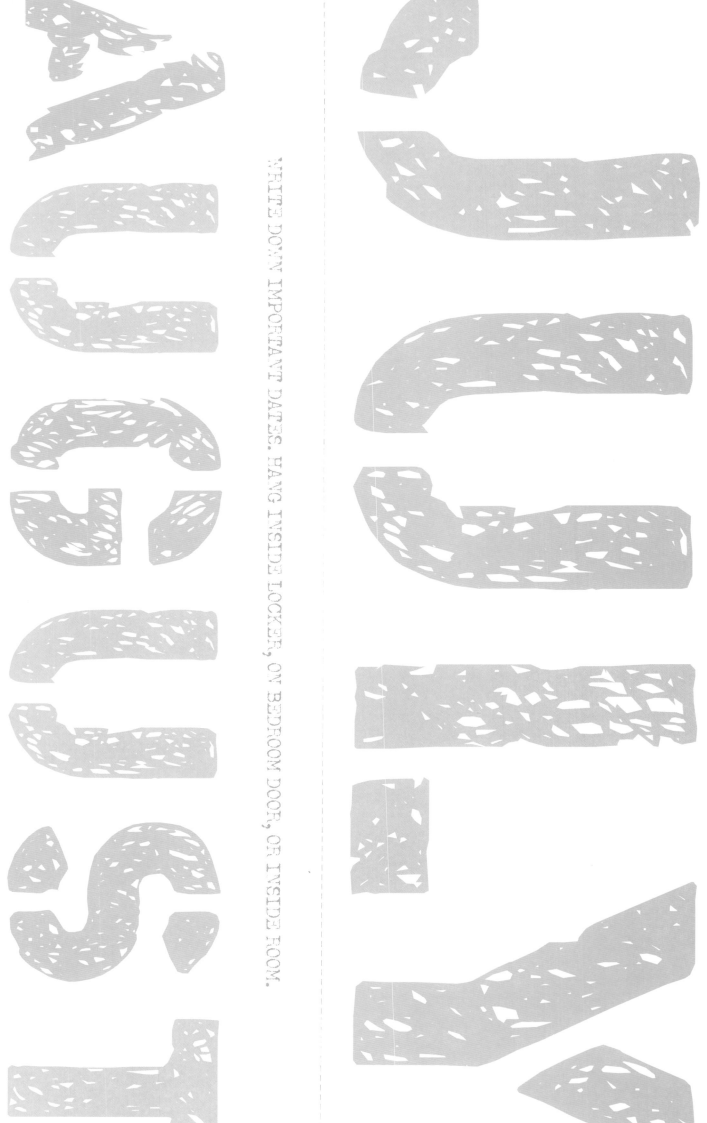

OLD SCHOOL
FALL TOO FAS
zero (nine)
Love is life's biggest adventure
RAD MOI
create A story

SEPTEMBER '09

1_____
2_____
3_____
4_____
5_____
6_____
7_____
8_____
9_____
10_____
11_____
12_____
13_____
14_____
15_____
16_____
17_____
18_____
19_____
20_____
21_____
22_____
23_____
24_____
25_____
26_____
27_____
28_____
29_____
30_____

OCTOBER '09

1_____
2_____
3_____
4_____
5_____
6_____
7_____
8_____
9_____
10_____
11_____
12_____
13_____
14_____
15_____
16_____
17_____
18_____
19_____
20_____
21_____
22_____
23_____
24_____
25_____
26_____
27_____
28_____
29_____
30_____
31_____

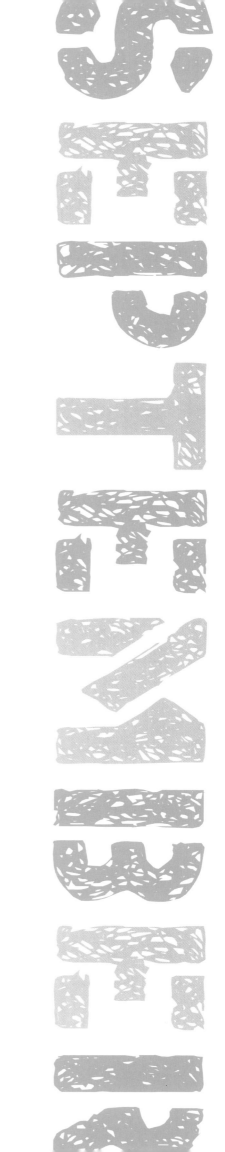

SEPTEMBER

WRITE DOWN IMPORTANT DATES. HANG INSIDE LOCKER, ON BEDROOM DOOR, OR INSIDE ROOM.

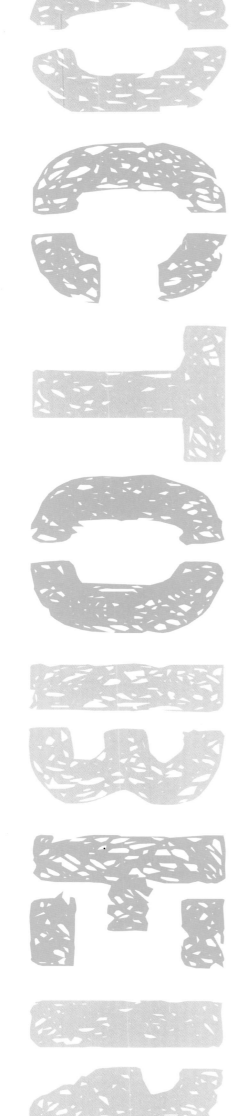

OCTOBER

WRITE DOWN IMPORTANT DATES. HANG INSIDE LOCKER, ON BEDROOM DOOR, OR INSIDE ROOM.

eleven

1_____
2_____
3_____
4_____
5_____
6_____
7_____
8_____
9_____
10_____
11_____
12_____
13_____
14_____
15_____
16_____
17_____
18_____
19_____
20_____
21_____
22_____
23_____
24_____
25_____
26_____
27_____
28_____
29_____
30_____

1_____
2_____
3_____
4_____
5_____
6_____
7_____
8_____
9_____
10_____
11_____
12_____
13_____
14_____
15_____
16_____
17_____
18_____
19_____
20_____
21_____
22_____
23_____
24_____
25_____
26_____
27_____
28_____
29_____
30_____
31_____

twelve

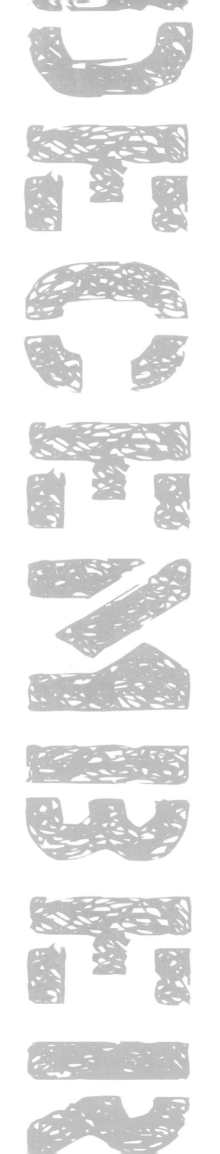

WRITE DOWN IMPORTANT DATES. HANG INSIDE LOCKER, ON BEDROOM DOOR, OR INSIDE ROOM.

WRITE DOWN IMPORTANT DATES. HANG INSIDE LOCKER, ON BEDROOM DOOR, OR INSIDE ROOM.